Letters to Home

Extending Math Beyond the Classroom

Mary Anne Mulder

Contents

MIMOSA
MOVING INTO
MATH
Kindergarten

Dear Teacher,

Included in this book are 35 "letters to home" that can be copied by you and distributed to the children in your class to take home to their families. There is one letter to accompany each of the 30 topics of the *Moving Into Math* program. The letters explain the concepts that the children have explored in class. Depending on the topic you are working on, the letters are accompanied by relevant activity sheets, or else they provide suggestions for activities that can be completed at home. By completing these activities at home with their families, your students will be able to share what they are learning in school. This family participation will encourage the children to talk about mathematical concepts, and will also reinforce the work done in class.

Occasionally, the children will also be requested to bring their completed activity sheets to school to share with the rest of the class. Many of the activity sheets are designed to be cut up to make games or cards, which can be kept at home for the children to use again later in the year.

This book also includes three letters asking families to contribute everyday materials that the class will need for use with *Moving Into Math*. I recommend that you send the first letter home in early September. This letter lists materials that are needed for the activities in topics 1-10. The second letter, which should be sent out in early November, lists the materials that are required to complete topics 11-20. The third letter, which relates to topics 21-30, should be sent out in early January.

Another special letter, which you will find at the back of this book, is an invitation to parents to visit your school and observe their child at work on a math activity.

All of the activities in this book are designed to develop mathematical language and problem-solving capabilities, helping to build a strong foundation of confidence and understanding for children's future work in mathematics. The emphasis is on informal, "real-world" situations, which will enable your students to "transfer" to their world at home what they have learned and discussed in the classroom. Each activity is designed to allow your students to explore beginning mathematical concepts in a way that is comfortable and appropriate for the ability of each child.

Some parents may feel that the activities in this book are "too easy" for their child. I recommend that you talk with these parents individually, to convey to them the idea that these activities are all designed to stimulate mathematical thinking and communication.

Here's to a productive, challenging, and exciting year of math!

Sincerely,

Mary Anne Mulder

Dear Family,

I am very pleased to have your child in my class this year. We will be using the Mimosa Kindergarten *Moving Into Math* program.

Moving Into Math is a new program which encourages children to talk about beginning math concepts as they explore new ideas and solve everyday problems.

I will be providing many opportunities for the children to share what we are doing in class with you at home. You can help by asking your child about activities he/she has been doing in school. This way, your involvement will boost your child's confidence as well as reinforce what we have discussed in class.

The year's program contains 30 topics. As we complete each one, I will send home a letter telling you what the children have been doing. Many of these letters will be accompanied by relevant activity sheets for your child to complete at home. Please read the directions to your child and either join in the activity or guide your child through it. The letters that are not accompanied by an activity sheet will provide suggestions for activities and discussion that can easily be incorporated into your everyday routines.

Many of the activity sheets your child brings home will be cut up to make games or cards. I suggest you keep these cards in a safe place so they can be used again during the year.

I believe your child can benefit the most when we work together as a team. Thank you for your time and cooperation. Here's to an exciting year of math!

Sincerely,

Dear Family,

The math program I'll be using with your child this year uses problem-solving activities to explore math ideas. Many of these activities require "hands-on" materials like those listed below. Could you please help contribute to our supply of classroom materials by having your child bring in as many as possible of the items I have checked below? Please choose items that are convenient for you to donate.

☐ reclosable sandwich bags

☐ shells

☐ cotton balls

☐ toilet paper rolls, wax paper rolls, or gift wrapping paper rolls

☐ old greeting cards

☐ small plastic animals

☐ plastic clip clothespins (1 package)

☐ small toy vehicles

☐ ribbon or string or rick rack

☐ hair barrettes

☐ small bean bags

☐ plastic jars of different sizes

☐ patterned fabric/material scraps

☐ wallpaper scraps

☐ small plastic containers with lids (for example, margarine tubs)

☐ animal cookie cutters

☐ old necklaces/earrings

☐ sandpaper

☐ whistles

☐ small empty boxes

☐ buttons

☐ newspapers, magazines, and advertisements

Thank you very much for helping to build our supply of everyday resources. It is extremely helpful if there are plenty of these materials available in the classroom so that the whole class can be involved in each activity.

Sincerely,

Dear Family,

This week the children have had a lot of fun looking at, handling, and describing various objects. The children have been using descriptive language related to many different attributes; for example:

- words related to size and length, such as *big, small, little, large, long, short, wide, narrow*
- words related to shape, such as *round, straight, curved, square*
- the names of colors
- words and phrases telling what things are made of, such as *made of paper/ plastic/wood*
- words describing sound such as *loud* and *soft*
- words describing texture, such as *smooth, soft, hard, scratchy.*

Being able to recognize an object's features will help the children with later math work that involves matching, sorting, and comparing.

You can help your child to have just as much fun exploring objects at home. For example, when your child is getting dressed, you both can talk about clothes using words such as "soft," "warm," "cool,"and "smooth," or words relating to the size and color of various items. When you and your child are looking at pictures in a book or magazine, invite your child to tell about objects in terms of their size, shape, or color. When you are driving or walking with your child, you can share and discuss the sights and sounds experienced along the way.

In this enjoyable and informal way, you and your child can share an appreciation of the world around you — and help to build important beginning concepts in math.

I appreciate your involvement with what we are doing at school. Have fun describing!

Sincerely,

Dear Family,

Over the last week, the children have been busy with activities that involve matching. They have been matching objects by looking at groups of things and finding two that are alike in some way. They have also gone on to match objects and pictures.

Matching skills come into play in the everyday real-world experiences of children, such as matching a button to a buttonhole, a cup to a saucer, or one color to the same color.

Matching activities are also important for later math work. For example, matching helps the children to identify features that they can use to sort objects. It also provides a foundation for work with numbers, when children will "match" different ways of showing the same number, such as a picture of three flowers, and the numeral "3."

Please help your child with the attached activity, which involves finding two objects that are the same in some way. Encourage your child to tell you how the objects are the same. Then he/she can draw them and bring the pictures to school to share.

Thanks for your help. Have fun!

Sincerely,

Matching Similar Objects

Have your child do the following:
- Find two things that are the same in some way.
- Tell you how they are alike.
- Draw pictures of them to bring to school to share.

© MIMOSA MOVING INTO MATH K **Activity Sheet 2.1**

Dear Family,

The children have been having a great time this week working on a range of sorting activities. Sorting is a more challenging task than matching, as the children are required to work with larger groups of objects.

We began with some basic sorting activities that involved sorting a group of objects according to one attribute; for example, sorting out the toy cars from a large pile of toys. The children have also experimented with grouping objects according to two or more attributes; for example, sorting stars by their size and color.

I have been encouraging the children to suggest and discuss different categories they can use when placing objects into piles or groups. Being able to carry out and describe these simple sorting activities will help the children to develop skills in classifying and using logic. These skills will eventually be used by the children to classify more abstract information and experiences in future mathematics work.

Please help your child play the accompanying sorting game. You can keep the game pieces in a plastic bag so that you can play it again another day.

Thank you very much for all your help.

Sincerely,

Sorting Picture Cards

- Help your child to cut out these cards and then have him/her sort them into groups; for example, the cards could be sorted into groups of animals, food, vehicles, etc., or into shaded/unshaded pictures, and so on.
- Have your child tell you how he/she sorted the cards.
- Play this game on another day, encouraging your child to find another way to sort the cards.

© MIMOSA MOVING INTO MATH K
Activity Sheet 3.1

Sorting Picture Cards

Dear Family,

The children have been reviewing and extending what they know about the numbers "one," "two," and "three" in class. Many children are able to "rote" count to much higher numbers when they start school, without really understanding what these numbers mean. It is very important that they acquire a genuine understanding of these numbers and feel confident working with them at this early stage.

The children have been practicing "one-to-one" counting with groups of objects. This involves giving one number name to each object in a group to determine how many objects there are in all.

Throughout the week, I have been giving the children many opportunities to handle groups of one, two, or three objects, and then matching these to numbers written as words and symbols. All of these activities have helped to develop your child's confidence in counting, naming, selecting, recognizing, and writing these early numbers.

We have also had fun practicing counting, or saying the numbers in their correct order, through rhymes and song.

Please help your child play the attached target game which is designed to give him/her additional practice with these early numbers.

Thank you for your help,

Yours sincerely,

Number Target

You will need a coin and some buttons to play this game.
- Take turns to throw the coin onto the target and collect the matching number of buttons from the pile.

- For example, if the coin lands on , collect 3 buttons.

- When all the buttons have been used, count the number of buttons in each collection aloud and find who has more.

This is a game that can be played again another day.

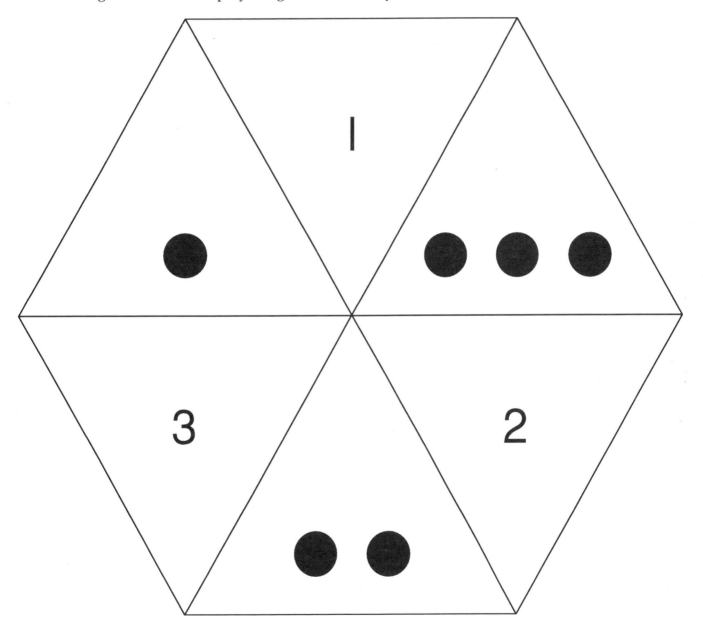

Dear Family,

Our class has been exploring positional terms such as, "top," "bottom," "over," "under," "above," "beside," "first," "last," "high," and "low." It is important for the children to develop a thorough understanding of positional language as it is used very frequently in math.

We have been working on many activities designed to help the children feel confident about using these terms. We have been making up stories and songs that include many of these terms and then acting them out together. The children have also been exploring the concepts of position and direction using concrete objects; for example, I have been asking them to place a certain color block "inside" or "outside" a box.

Please keep in mind that it may take several months for all of these terms to be fully understood by your child. You can help him/her learn to use these terms at home as you talk about everyday activities. For example, you could say, "Put your toys inside the toy box," instead of the more general direction, "Put your toys here."

The accompanying activity is designed to be completed in a fun and relaxed way. As your child colors the picture, you should discuss the position of the objects in the picture with him/her in an informal way. Please do not worry about your child's coloring skills; the focus of this activity should be on developing his/her understanding of positional language.

Thank you again for your time and cooperation.

Sincerely,

Discussing the Picture

- Have your child color this picture using crayons or pencils.
- As your child is coloring, ask him/her about the section being colored, using words that refer to position: above, below, under, over, inside, outside, high, low, and so on. For example, your child may say, " The rainbow goes over the house."

Dear Family,

Our class has been busy investigating the language that is used to describe opposites; for example, "long" and "short," "far" and "near," "big and little," "hot" and "cold," "left" and "right." Being able to use these everyday terms will help children with later math work that involves measurement or direction.

As you know, our math program places a strong emphasis on language development, since children's understanding of a mathematical concept depends on their understanding of the language associated with that concept.

You can help your child become confident with using the language of opposites. Here are some suggestions:

• Ask your child to set the table tonight. Tell him/her to put the fork on the left side of the plate and the knife and spoon on the right side of the plate.

• When your child brushes his/her teeth, suggest brushing the left side first and then the right side.

• Discuss the relative sizes of toys in your child's room. Ask him/her to show you a big toy and then a small toy. Ask your child to look around the room and tell you something that is up high and something that is down low.

• Ask your child to look inside the refrigerator and tell you something that is on the top shelf and something that is on the bottom shelf.

• Talk about hot and cold when you are cooking. Have your child tell you which foods are hot and which are cold at meal times.

• Have your child put on or take off the left sock and shoe and then the right sock and shoe.

• Have your child walk outside the house and then inside the house.

These fun and informal activities can be incorporated into your everyday routine with little disruption.

I really appreciate your involvement in what we are doing at school. Your efforts are helping your child to develop a deeper understanding of the world and to build a foundation for future success in mathematics.

Sincerely,

Dear Family,

The children have been having lots of fun comparing the sizes of various objects in class; for example, the length of pieces of string or the width of different leaves. Through these kinds of experiences, the children have developed an understanding of the language of comparison. Instead of simply describing a piece of ribbon as "long" or "short," they have been comparing it to another ribbon and describing it as "longer" or "shorter."

The children began by working with hands-on materials only, so that they could handle each object and feel confident about the comparisons they made. The class then went on to make comparisons using pictures of objects. The children also had experiences with selecting the appropriate word card to match a comparison situation. These activities have also extended the children's ability to estimate the size and length of different items. At this stage, the children have only been required to compare two objects at a time.

Please help your child complete the following activity which will allow him/her to compare the length or width of objects found around your home, with the lizard and the frog that he/she cuts out.

Thanks once again for all your help — I really appreciate it. I feel that your child learns best when we work together as a team.

Sincerely,

Comparing Width and Length

Help your child to:
- Cut out the lizard and the frog along the dotted lines.
- Find things around the house that are:
    longer or shorter than the lizard
    wider or narrower than the frog

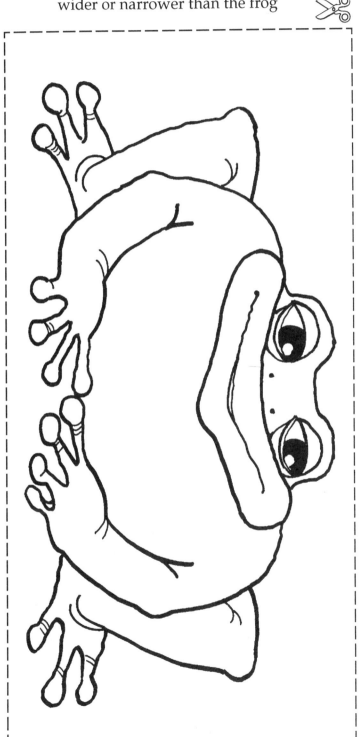

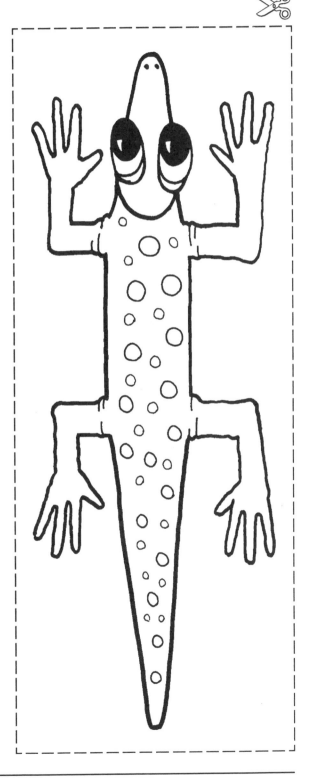

Dear Family,

During the last week the children have been busy investigating the number four. They began by reviewing their knowledge of the numbers one, two, and three, and then went on to work on a range of activities that included:

  making collections of three and four using everyday objects;

  selecting or creating pictures that show groups of three or four;

  seeing the number words "three" and "four" written in context;

  identifying and naming dot pictures for the number four;

  recognizing the number symbol "4" and learning how to write it.

These activities have helped to develop the children's estimation skills as well as their understanding that a number can be shown in many different ways. These kinds of experiences also help to develop your child's "number awareness," that is, their ability to picture and work with numbers in their minds.

After many experiences with objects, pictures, and dot cards, the children are now at a stage where they can recognize a group of four objects without having to count them. This ability provides a foundation for the introduction of higher numbers later this year. For example, when we begin learning about the number seven, the children will use their knowledge of the number four when counting groups of seven objects. They will be able to begin by counting four of the objects together as "four . . ." and then counting on ". . . five, six, seven. There are seven."

Please help your child play the attached game at home, so that he/she gains extra practice with the numbers three and four. You may wish to keep the game pieces in a reclosable envelope or bag so that you can play the game together another day.

Thanks again for your time and cooperation. I am sure that it means a lot to your child.

Sincerely,

Sorting Into Groups

Help your child do the following:
- Cut out the cards on this activity sheet and activity sheet 8.2.
- Use the cards to play different games. These could include:
    - Sorting the cards into groups by picture or number
    - Using buttons to show how many things are on each card

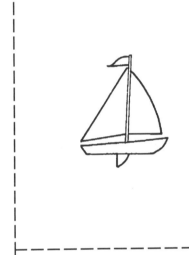

Name _____

Cards for Sorting into Groups

© MIMOSA MOVING INTO MATH K
Activity Sheet 8.2

Dear Family,

The children have been busy discussing the concept of ordering in class. The ability to order events is important for understanding the concept of time and duration. It is also essential that the children can order events before they are introduced to ordinal numbers ("first," "second," "third," etc.). The children will use ordering and sequencing skills in future math work when they are required to follow a series of steps in order to solve a problem.

We have been working on various activities that involve ordering; for example, the children have been talking about events that take place at different times of the day or week, as well as the sequence of events in familiar stories. I have also been giving the children picture cards that depict a sequence of events and asking them to arrange these in the correct order.

Please encourage your child to discuss the events of his/her day with you. Not only does this keep you informed about his/her learning, but it also gives your child practice verbalizing what he/she has learned. You may wish to share your day's experiences with your child. He/she can then see how you order the events of your day and that you are using math too.

Attached is an activity sheet which features four picture cards. Please help your child to cut these out and then arrange them in an logical order. Have your child tell you his/her thinking as you complete the activity together.

Thanks again for your cooperation. I hope that you learn from each other.

Sincerely,

Ordering Pictures

Help your child do the following:
- Cut out the picture cards below.
- Put the cards in order. (This can be done in two ways.)
- Have your child tell you how he/she put the cards in order.

© MIMOSA MOVING INTO MATH K

Dear Family,

During the past few days the children have been using everything that they have learned this year about math. As you know, the children have already had many experiences identifying, describing, and comparing the attributes of different objects. They also had some experiences with ordering events. This week the children have been building on these experiences as they investigated the more challenging task of ordering objects according to size and length.

The children began by ordering groups of three objects; for example, lengths of ribbon, cardboard boxes, and bottles filled with rice, according to their length, size, or weight. They naturally approached each ordering task by identifying the item at each extreme; for example, the biggest and the smallest, and then looked at whatever came in between. This kind of activity provided many opportunities for the children to discuss what they were doing. They also explored different ways of ordering the same things; for example, three boxes could be stacked, put in a row, or placed one inside the other.

The children then moved on to ordering a larger number of objects using what they had discovered about ordering three objects. For example, to order five lengths of ribbon, the children first identified the longest and shortest ribbons. Then they placed the other ribbons, one by one, in between the first two ribbons, making sure that there was a longer ribbon on one side and a shorter ribbon on the other each time.

You can help your child extend his/her knowledge of ordering at home. Ask your child to find five drinking glasses that are the same and then arrange these in a row. Help him/her to pour water into each glass so that they are in order from full to almost empty. As you do this, discuss the amount of water in each glass and how it compares to the amount of water in the other glasses.

Have fun and thank you for your time!

Sincerely,

Dear Family,

We are already one third of the way through our math program, and we are once again in need of some materials for our classroom math supplies. I would greatly appreciate it if your child could bring in as many as possible of the items checked below.

- ☐ material/cloth scraps
- ☐ small pieces of old tile
- ☐ gift wrapping paper
- ☐ shoelaces
- ☐ egg cartons
- ☐ old bead necklaces
- ☐ paper plates
- ☐ sponges
- ☐ popsicle or craft sticks
- ☐ milk cartons
- ☐ sawdust
- ☐ sand
- ☐ wooden clothespins
- ☐ reclosable sandwich bags
- ☐ pipe cleaners
- ☐ calendars
- ☐ buttons
- ☐ cookie cutters
- ☐ opaque plastic bottles
- ☐ magnets

Thank you very much for your cooperation. Your contributions have really helped us out!

Sincerely,

Dear Family,

Our class has been having a lot of fun exploring patterns this week. In the process, the children have reinforced other work that they have done this year; for example, they have extended what they know about comparing, sorting, and matching different objects, and they reviewed their knowledge of positional and directional terms. These skills help the children to recognize and describe how certain shapes are arranged to form a pattern, and how the shapes in a pattern relate to one another.

The children began by looking for patterns that occur in the world around them. These included patterns in the classroom (such as patterns in the bricks or curtains), and patterns in nature (such as patterns in leaves, or stripes on animals). They then began making their own patterns, copying other patterns, and finally extending patterns using paints, blocks, beads, macaroni noodles, and other hands-on materials.

These activities form the basis of pattern work which will be continued in Grade 1, when the emphasis will be on creating and extending patterns, as well as finding missing elements in patterns.

At this stage, the children are working with hands-on materials only. Working with pictures and patterns will come at a later stage of your child's development.

You can help your child build on his/her understanding of patterns by identifying and discussing patterns around your home, on fabrics and so on. You can also have a lot of fun with your child creating patterns from household items such as shoes, socks, silverware, and washcloths. Ask him/her to describe the pattern to you.

Thanks for your time and cooperation. Have fun discovering patterns together with your child.

Sincerely,

Dear Family,

This week, the children have been very active locating and describing solid shapes such as spheres, cubes, cylinders, and pyramids.

At this stage, the children have not been using formal terms to describe these solid shapes; instead, I have been encouraging the children to use their own words, such as "can shaped," "ball shaped," and "box shaped."

The children have been having a lot of fun using their own bodies to act out the appearance of solid shapes. For example, they can extend their arms upward with their fingertips touching so that they form a sharp point like that of a pyramid. There have also been many opportunities for the children to practice positional language in class. For example, I have asked the children to make a pretend ball with their hands and then put it above their heads or under their desks.

During our discussions, the children have also encountered some "plane shapes" (two-dimensional or flat shapes), such as the circle at each end of a cylinder, the square or rectangle on the side of a box-shape, or the triangle on the side of a pyramid.

Your child will be relating solid shapes to plane shapes in the accompanying activity. Please remember that the emphasis is on observing and talking about shapes in an informal way. Begin by conducting a shape hunt around your home. Together with your child, go looking for cylinders, spheres, cubes, and pyramids — you will find that your kitchen cupboards are full of shapes! As your child finds different solid shapes, have him/her place them on or near the shape outlines on the attached activity sheet.

Thanks once again for all your help. Your child gains a lot when you discuss these beginning math concepts at home. This extra attention helps to show your child how math is used beyond the classroom.

Sincerely,

Solid Shape Hunt

Help your child to:
- Find some examples of cubes, spheres, cylinders, or pyramids around your home.
- Place each object on or near the matching plane shape below, e.g. a box shape on the square, a pyramid on the triangle.

Dear Family,

Our class has been very busy learning more about the numbers one, two, three, and four. In particular, I have been making sure that the children have had many experiences with the number symbols (1, 2, 3, and 4) and number words for one, two, three, and four. It is important that the children understand that there are different ways of representing a single number.

The children have been involved in matching activities where they have had to match picture cards, word cards, and symbol cards for example:

 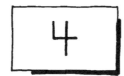 

I have also been reading the children lots of stories and poems that include these numbers both in symbol and word form.

At this stage, there is no need to worry about your child's ability to write the number words and symbols. It is more important that he/she displays a sound understanding of these numbers and what they represent.

The accompanying activity sheet features a number-word die that you can make for your child using scissors and glue. The instructions for playing a game using the die are written on the activity sheet. Have fun!

Thank you for your cooperation.

Sincerely,

Number Word Game

Cut out the number word die, fold the tabs, and glue the sides together. To play the Number Word Game, you will need some pieces of cereal.

- Each person takes a turn at tossing the die then collecting the matching number of cereal pieces.
- When every player has had four turns, the player with the most cereal pieces is the winner.

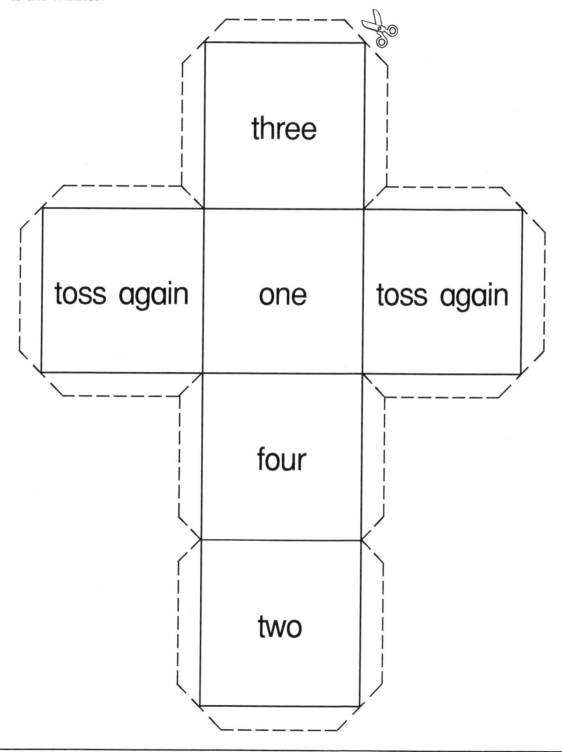

Dear Family,

The children have been spending a lot of time learning about the number "five" over the last week. They have been involved in recognizing, naming, and creating groups of five objects. They have also been locating real-world examples of the number five, such as the number of fingers on a hand, or the number of toes on a foot.

As with the numbers three and four, the children began by working on activities designed to ensure that they could associate the spoken number word "five" with a collection of five objects. As the children developed confidence working with groups or pictures of five objects, I introduced the symbol for the number five (5) to them.

Throughout the last few days, I have been using the number five frequently in various contexts. To extend their understanding of five, we have been reading and discussing many stories, poems, and nursery rhymes that feature five. I have also been encouraging the children to create their own stories and rhymes about the number five, although they have not been expected to write the word "five" at this stage.

The attached activity is designed so that your child can find groups of five and then draw as many groups of five as he/she wants.

Sincerely,

The Five House

- Help your child find groups of five by counting the different objects. He/she can color the groups of five things.
- Encourage your child to draw more groups of five; for example, five apples on the tree, five cats on the sidewalk.
- Ask your child to tell about the groups he/she has drawn.

Signature _____ Date _____

Dear Family,

The children have been continuing to learn about relating numbers to groups of objects during the last few days. I have been integrating all of the aspects of number awareness that the children have developed throughout this year through work with hands-on materials, pictures, words, and symbols. The children also began to explore the number "six."

To help the children feel confident in working with the number six, I introduced it to them in the same way as I introduced the numbers three, four, and five. The children began by using hands-on materials to make groups of six and associating these with the number word "six." They gradually progressed to recognizing and writing the number symbol "6."

It is important to know that the numbers beyond five are much more difficult than the numbers one through five. Adults and children alike find it difficult to say how many objects there are in a group of more than five without counting. For this reason, I have been giving the children plenty of experiences working with groups of six. This has involved arranging the same group of six items in many different ways, and allowing the children to count the group each time to reinforce the idea that the total number does not change.

As always, we have focused on experiences with language as these help to develop the children's confidence with number words. The children have been enjoying listening to many poems and rhymes that focus on the numbers one through to six.

You can help your child continue his/her learning of the numbers one, two, three, four, five, and six at home by helping him/her complete the attached activity. This activity focuses on language in math and is aimed at showing your child the importance of numbers in the "real" world.

Thanks for your cooperation!

Sincerely,

Domino Games

Help your child to:
- Cut out the dominoes along the dotted lines.
- Join the dominoes together
  in different ways; for example:

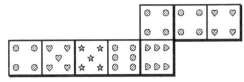

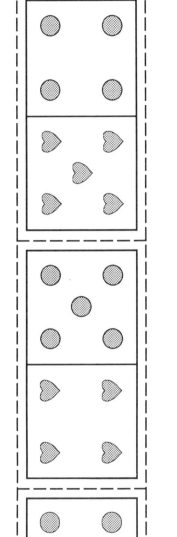
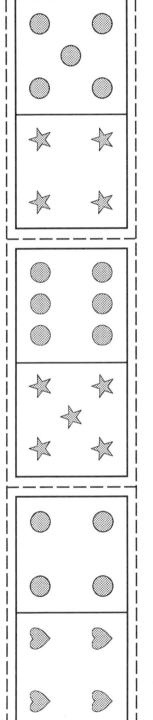
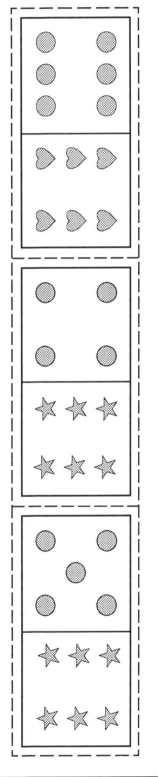
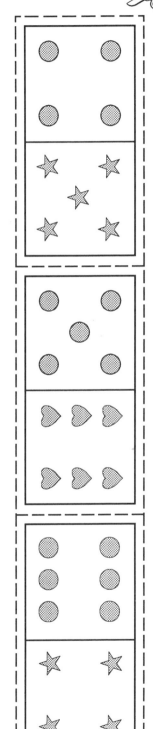

Activity Sheet 15.1

Dear Family,

Our class has been very busy investigating and describing triangles, squares, and circles this week. These observations are an extension of the children's earlier work with spheres, cubes, pyramids, and cylinders.

Some of the different activities the children have recently been working on include:

> using their bodies to make squares, circles, and triangles;
>
> recognizing and identifying these shapes;
>
> matching shapes of the same kind;
>
> discussing the different characteristics of squares, circles, and triangles;
>
> making squares, circles, and triangles out of hands-on materials; for example, blocks and modeling clay;
>
> creating pictures using squares, circles, and triangles.

All of these activities have generated much discussion in our classroom as the children have been identifying and talking about the characteristics of these shapes. For example, the children have been saying things like, *All of these shapes have four sharp points* (corners). *The shapes look like windows,* and so on.

Please encourage your child to tell you about what he/she has been doing with shapes at school. I believe that your child really benefits from sharing his/her learning experiences with you at home. Attached is a shape hunt activity for you to complete with your child.

Thank you again for your time.

Sincerely,

Shape Hunt

Go on a shape hunt with your child.
- As you walk around the house look for the shapes shown below.
- Have your child draw an example of each shape in the middle column.
- For each extra shape you find put a check in the last column.

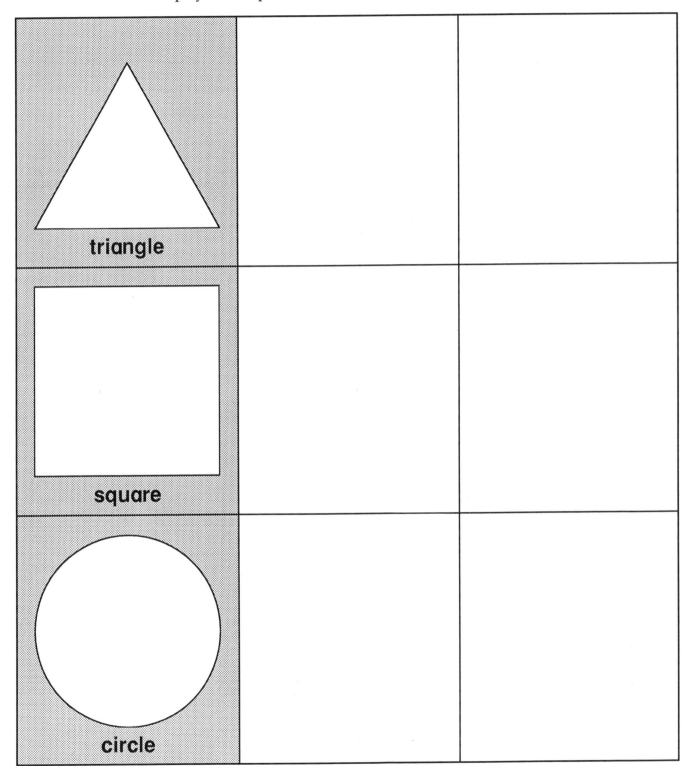

Dear Family,

Our class has been busy exploring the concepts of "more" and "less" in terms of capacity, weight, and number.

The children began by comparing the capacity of many different containers, using materials such as water, sand, or clay and carrying out actions like filling, emptying, fitting in, packing, and estimating available space.

Many of these activities were simply extensions of free play and the children were encouraged to use their natural language to describe what they were doing. This included using expressions such as: *full, empty, part full, nearly full, overflowing, enough, too much, all, a lot, a little,* and so on.

The children have also had many opportunities to handle different objects as they explored more and less in relation to weight. It is much harder for children to judge the weight of an object simply by looking at it. In Grade 1, the children will be using a balance to measure and compare the weights of different objects, but at this stage their goal is to develop confidence using terms such as *heavy, light, weighs more,* and *weighs less* as they hold an object in their hands.

The children also investigated more and less in regard to number. They used links, counters, blocks, and other classroom objects to compare the numbers one through six. These activities have contributed to the children's developing number awareness and also encouraged them to use language such as *many, few, more,* and *less.*

You can use the accompanying chart with your child to explore the concepts of more and less at home. It can be used whenever your child is comparing the capacity, weight, or number of any objects small enough to fit on the chart. For example:

• You could put a glass full of water on the side that says "more" and then ask your child to put a smaller glass of water on the side that says "less."

• Heavier objects can be placed on the "more" side while lighter objects can be placed on the "less" side.

• Your child could also use this chart with counters, beans, or pieces of cereal to explore more and less with numbers. For example, you could put three pieces of cereal on the "less" side, and then ask your child to put more pieces of cereal on the other side.

Thank you so much for your time.

Sincerely,

More or Less

Your child can place objects on this chart to act out comparisons of capacity, weight, and number.

more	less

Activity Sheet 17.1

Dear Family,

Over the last few days, the children have been busy looking at the ordinal numbers "first," "second," "third," and "last."

At this stage the children's exploration of ordinal numbers is restricted to these four for several reasons. Firstly, the children are more likely to be familiar with these already through everyday experiences, such as running races. These ordinal number names are also the most difficult to associate with the matching counting number. For example, the word "one" does not sound or look like the word "first." The later ordinal number names such as fourth, fifth, sixth, and so on, more closely resemble number names and will be relatively easy for the children to remember.

The children have been having fun acting out ordinal positions in many different ways; for example, they have been arranging objects in the positions of first, second, third, and last. They have also been pointing to objects and pictures and using the words first, second, third, and last, to describe their positions.

At this stage, we will only be using the *words*, not the symbolic ordinal numbers 1st, 2nd, and 3rd.

Please find attached some ribbons for the ordinal numbers, first, second, third, and last, for your child to cut out and color. These ribbons can be used whenever your child is arranging objects in a row. Please encourage him/her to work from left to right when ordering objects, as with reading or writing. Your child may need some help reading the ordinal words on the ribbons even though he/she has been using these at school.

You can help your child develop his/her confidence with ordinal numbers by completing some of these suggested activities together.

• Arrange a plate, fork, spoon, and cup so that the fork is first, the plate second, the cup third, and the spoon last.

• Now put the cup first, the spoon second, the fork third, and the plate last.

- Then put the plate away first, the fork away second, the spoon away third, and the cup away last.

- As your child is getting ready for bed, have him/her take off the left shoe first, then the left sock second, then the right shoe third, and so on.

- Ask your child to stage a race for his/her toy animals. Encourage him/her to tell you which toys come first, second, and last.

Thank you once again for your help!

Sincerely,

Name _____

Ordinal Ribbons

Your child can use these ribbons whenever he/she has arranged items in a row.
Be sure to read the labels aloud to your child so that he/she gains experience in
recognizing these words.

Dear Family

The children have been very active during the last week exploring the number "seven." They have been following a similar sequence of activities to those used to introduce them to the numbers one through six. By using the same approach each time a new number is introduced, the children can confidently refer to their past experiences.

As in earlier weeks, the children have been working with hands-on materials, such as counters or toys, to represent different numbers. This has involved naming and comparing groups of seven and then matching these to a picture of a group of seven. The children have also had many opportunities to use the spoken and written number word for seven and I have recently introduced them to the number symbol "7."

All of these activities have greatly stimulated the children's enthusiasm and thinking about numbers. They have also reinforced their understanding that a single number can be shown in many different ways.

As always, the children have been having many creative language experiences. We have been reading stories and rhymes that include the number seven; these experiences are not only a way of showing the children number words in context, they have also inspired them to make up their own stories about numbers.

The list of activities below provides many suggestions for reinforcing your child's understanding of the number seven. Many of these can be incorporated into your everyday routines.

Have your child complete at least seven of these activities:

• Go outside and run around the house seven times.

• Go outside and find seven rocks and then show them to you. Have him/her count them aloud for you.

• Collect seven of his/her favorite toys and then count these for you.

• Name seven of his/her friends.

- Brush or comb his/her hair seven times.

- Find seven objects in your house that are the same. Have him/her tell you how these things are the same.

- Find seven glasses in the kitchen. Have him/her tell you how these are similar or different.

- Look in a phone book and find a phone number with the number symbol 7 in it.

- Show you seven of his/her toes.

- Tell you seven different things that he/she really likes to eat.

- Draw the number symbol 7 on your back with his/her finger.

- Find the number symbol 7 in a newspaper and then circle it.

- Count aloud from one to seven.

- Look at a calendar and point out the number symbol 7 to you.

Thank you once again for your assistance.

Sincerely,

Dear Family,

The children have been very active with their investigation of numbers. During the past few days, they have been exploring the number "eight." This exploration included a review of all the numbers they have covered this year as they looked at how this new number can be represented by groups of objects. For example, I have been giving the children instructions such as, *Make one more than seven*, or *Make two groups of four*, when they have been arranging objects into groups. In this way, they have come to see how the number eight relates to the numbers below it.

The children have also been matching the number word "eight" and the number symbol "8" with the number eight represented by picture and dot cards. These cards show different arrangements of eight, such as two groups of four, or a row of five and a row of three. These kinds of activities reinforce the idea that a large number such as eight can be represented in a variety of ways.

Each time the children worked on an activity, they were encouraged to say how many were in each group, and how many there were in all. The children have also been looking at and discussing many real-world examples of the number eight; for example, the number of legs on an octopus or a spider. As the children's ability to use mathematical language develops, their number awareness and problem-solving skills also improve.

Your child can extend his/her awareness of the number symbol "8" by circling all the "8s" he/she can find in a newspaper or catalog at home. The accompanying activity sheet will reinforce the numbers five through eight for your child. He/she will need a pile of edibles (raisins, pieces of cereal, nuts, or small crackers) to complete this activity.

Your help, as always, is greatly appreciated. Have fun and try to encourage your child to use as much language as possible.

Sincerely,

Eight Puzzle

- Read the words in the eight puzzle aloud to your child.
- Help him/her to put the correct number of edibles on each part of the puzzle.
- If your child wishes he/she can cut out the puzzle pieces and then reassemble the number symbol eight.

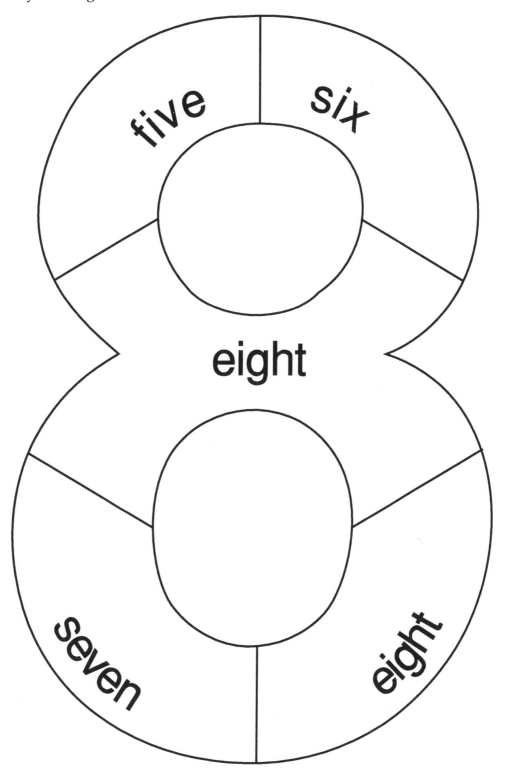

© MIMOSA MOVING INTO MATH K

Dear Family,

As we approach the final part of our math program, I am once again in need of some materials for our classroom. It would be very helpful if your child could bring in as many as possible of the items I have checked below.

- [ ] old animal cookie cutters
- [ ] ribbon
- [ ] wooden and plastic clothespins
- [ ] fabric scraps
- [ ] sponges
- [ ] egg cartons
- [ ] burlap
- [ ] empty food boxes, cans, jars, or bottles
- [ ] reclosable sandwich bags
- [ ] acorns
- [ ] shells

Thank you once again for you help and support. It is greatly appreciated.

Sincerely,

Dear Family,

We have been very busy learning about and exploring the number "nine" in class. The number nine is far more challenging than any of the numbers the children have encountered so far. It is very difficult for children and adults alike to recognize a group of nine objects without counting them, except when they are arranged as three rows of three.

The children have been working with and creating many different arrangements of nine objects and this has contributed greatly to their understanding of nine. I truly believe that the children learn more when they are encouraged to use hands-on materials to explore new concepts. I also believe that children can learn a lot by sharing their ideas with each other.

I have been continuing to give the children a wide range of language experiences. They have really enjoyed listening to me read stories, poems, and rhymes about the number nine. They have also had a lot of fun making up their own stories. After we read together in class, we always take the time to discuss what we have read or created. In this way, we all learn from each other!

You can help your child continue his/her learning at home by reading stories or poems that talk about the number nine and the other numbers we have explored together so far. Try to make time to have a discussion after you and your child read something together.

The attached activity is intended to help build your child's awareness of the number nine. Have fun learning together!

Sincerely,

Making Nine

Help your child to:
- Count how many things there are in each group.
- Draw more pictures to make groups of nine.

Activity Sheet 21.1

Dear Family,

We have been continuing our study of the numbers one through nine during our school day. The children have also been introduced to the number "zero." Most of the children already had some idea of what the word zero meant; many of them had heard a count-down for a rocket launch that ended in zero. Together we practiced saying count-downs and this really helped to reinforce the position and value of the number zero in relation to the other numbers the children have explored so far this year.

The children are all very curious about the number zero. We have been having many informal discussions where the children and I have been having fun making up questions that have zero as the answer. For example, *How many real dinosaurs are in our classroom? How many real snakes are there in our classroom? If I shoot this basketball towards the hoop and I miss, how many points will I score?*

As another way of demonstrating zero, I have showed the children an empty plate and asked them questions such as, *How many cookies do you see?* or *How many pieces of fruit are on my plate?* The children responded by answering: *no cookies, none,* or *zero pieces of fruit* each time. These kinds of questions have helped the children to see how the concept of zero is used all the time in everyday life.

These activities have really contributed to the children's understanding of the important number zero. The children will be using zero frequently in Grade 1 when they learn about two-digit numbers that end in a zero, such as 20 and 30.

You can help build on your child's understanding of zero at home by completing the attached activity together.

Sincerely,

Count your Toys

For this activity your child will need a bath towel and nine small toys.
Have him/her arrange the toys on the floor.
Read the following instructions aloud.

- Cover two toys with the towel.

- Now cover five toys with the towel.

- Now cover seven toys with the towel.

- Uncover the toys and put one toy on top of the towel.

- Now put the towel under three toys.

- Put four toys beside the towel.

- Put zero toys on the towel.

- Put six toys in your right hand and the towel on your head.

- Put the towel under your feet and put zero toys on your head.

- Put nine toys under the towel.

- Put five of the toys away.

- Put three toys away.

- Cover the last toy with the towel.

- Write the number 0 on my back with your finger.

© MIMOSA MOVING INTO MATH K

Dear Family

Over the last few days, the children have been exploring the concept of addition in a fun and informal way. They have been working on activities that involve combining and joining two groups of objects. They have had many opportunities to work with hands-on materials such as cubes, clothespins, counters, and so on, to act out addition stories. They did this by making two groups of objects and counting how many objects were in each group. Then they combined the two groups and counted how many there were in all.

As they worked together, I encouraged them to talk about what they were doing in their own words. These included expressions such as: *put together, in all, join together, altogether,* and *add*. The term *plus* is not introduced in Kindergarten, as it is not part of the children's natural language. The children will learn to use the formal mathematical terms for addition and the symbol "+" in Grade 1.

This beginning addition work has been fun for the children and me. After the children had a lot of practice counting groups of real objects, they moved on to counting pictures, and then combining and joining sets of pictures.

Some of the children dictated their own number stories for me to record and they also drew pictures to illustrate these stories.

Please encourage your child to tell you what has been happening at school. He/she will be encouraged to share some other school experiences with you if you show an interest.

You can help your child continue his/her learning at home by playing the accompanying game together.

Sincerely,

Going Fishing

Please help your child to cut out the fish on Activity sheet 23.2. Tell him/her to put all the fish next to the lake. (Activity sheet 23.3)   Read the following addition stories to your child and have him/her act these out using the fish and the lake.

Encourage your child to tell you the total number of fish at the end of each story. Also, make sure that he/she has the lake clear of fish before you begin each story.

1. Three fish were swimming in the lake. Suddenly three more fish came swimming by. How many fish are there in the lake now?

2. Two fish were asleep in the water. Then, four fish came swimming by and woke them up. How many fish are awake in all?

3. Five fish were playing in the lake. Three other fish swam by and invited them to a party. They all went to the party together. How many fish went to the party?

4. Seven fish were eating dinner in the lake. Two more fish came by and decided to join them. How many fish are eating dinner together?

You might like to play this game on another day, making up more fish stories with your child.

Fish cards for Going Fishing

Lake for Going Fishing

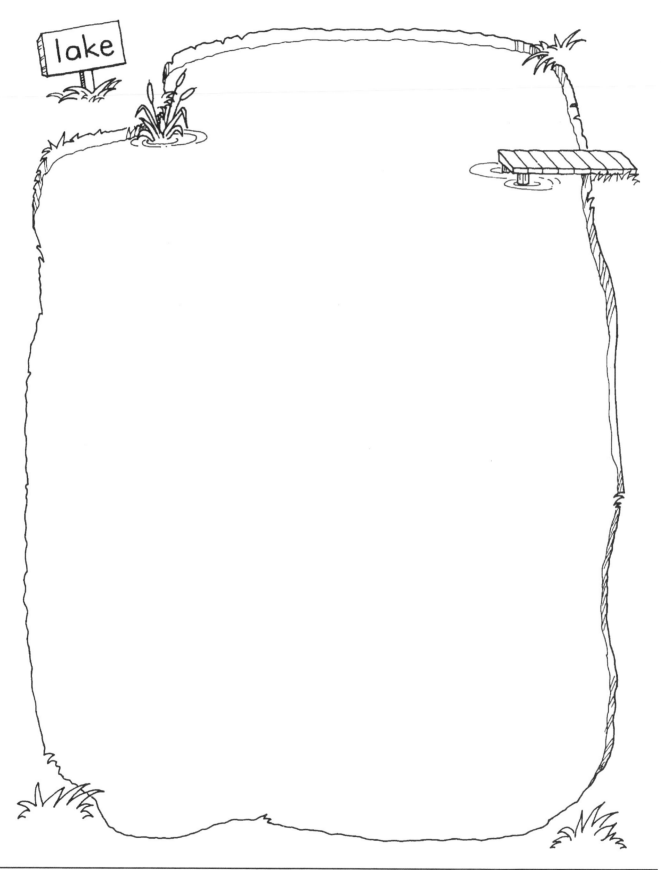

Activity Sheet 23.3

Dear Family,

After the children explored the concept of addition, they went on to look at subtraction. As with addition, the children have developed an understanding of the subtraction process by being involved in activities which used hands-on materials such as counters, blocks, or beans. The children have had a lot of fun acting out subtraction stories using these kinds of materials.

Many of the stories I told them were "real-world" experiences; for example, *Five birds were in a tree. Two flew away. Then there were three.* They began their stories by telling and showing how many they started with, taking some away, and finally, counting how many were left. They also made up their own "take-away" stories which they shared with each other.

You can help your child continue to learn about subtraction at home by using the attached activity sheet. Your child will need nine small cookies or crackers. Encourage him/her to tell you some subtraction stories that involve the cookies and the cookie jar. (Activity Sheet 24.1)   For example, *I had nine cookies. My sister was hungry so I let her eat three of them. Now I only have six cookies in my jar.* In this example, he/she should start with nine cookies on the cookie jar picture and then take away three of them to leave six.

Continue to encourage your child to tell you what he/she is doing at school. This will help build his/her language skills as well as inform you of day-to-day classroom experiences.

Sincerely,

Taking Away Cookies

© MIMOSA MOVING INTO MATH K **Activity Sheet 24.1**

Dear Family,

The children have been busy building on what they learned earlier in the year about comparing more or less, and the concept of ordering. In previous weeks they compared the capacity and weight of two different objects, and matched and ordered objects.

During the past few days, the class has been focusing on comparing and ordering numbers. The children have been using hands-on materials to compare different numbers; for example, I asked them to arrange clothespins into two groups and then tell me which group had more and which group had less. During our discussions, I encouraged the children to use words like *greater, fewer, the same number, more, less, equal, not as many, too many, most, fewest, greatest,* and *least* when making comparisons.

Initially I asked the children to compare numbers with large differences, such as three compared with eight. They then went on to make more difficult comparisons such as four compared with five. The children also had many opportunities to compare picture and dot cards. After many of these experiences, the children have developed the ability to order number pictures by sight.

Together we made a classroom graph which we called, *My Favorite Animal.* I asked all of the children to draw a picture of their favorite animal. These pictures were then sorted into groups, such as zoo animals and farm animals. We created a pictograph by pasting each group in a row on a big sheet of tagboard. The children were then able to compare the number of animals in each group and answer questions such as, *Which group has more? How many more? How do you know?*

You can help your child compare numbers at home by playing the attached card game. Also, please try to use some of the terms mentioned above as you complete this activity with your child, and whenever possible during the day. Using these words at home will help your child to see the connection between math and the "real" world. Thanks for your help and support. It is greatly appreciated.

Sincerely,

Comparing Numbers Game (two players)

Help your child to:
- Cut out the number cards on Activity Sheets 25.2 and 25.3.
- Shuffle the cards and then deal them into equal piles. Make sure that the piles are face down.

To play the game:
- Each player turns the card on top of their pile over.
- The player who has the card with the higher number on it takes both cards and places them at the bottom of his/her pile of cards.
- If both cards show the same number then players return their cards to the bottom of their pile of cards.
- The player who ends up with all the cards is the winner.

After playing this game several times, you can change the rules slightly to play another game. This time, the player with the smaller number on his/her card gets to keep both cards after each turn.

Cards for Comparing Numbers Game

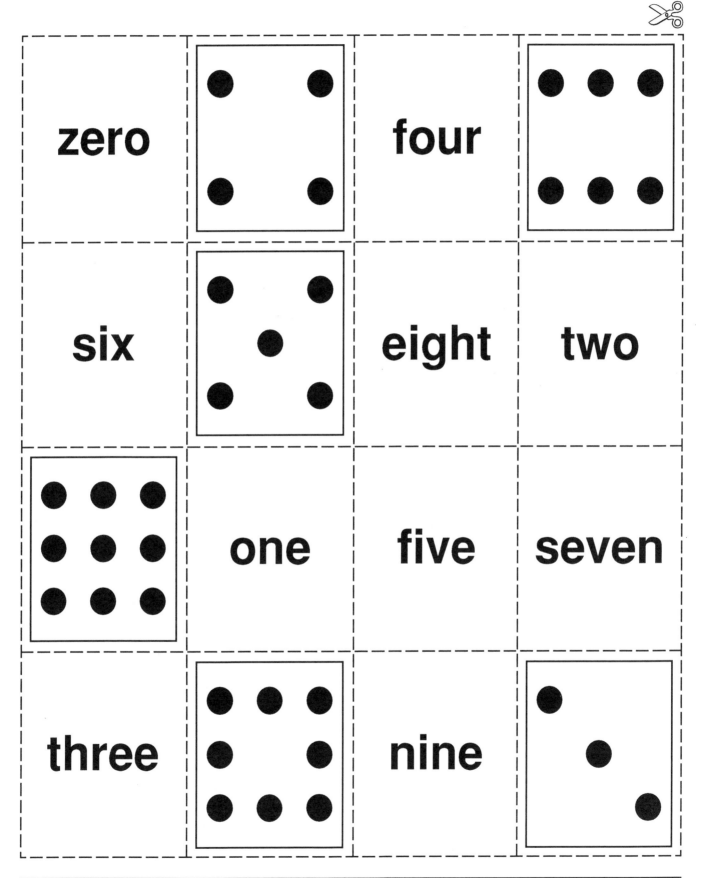

© MIMOSA MOVING INTO MATH K

Cards for Comparing Numbers Game

	9	**1**	**2**
	0	**3**	**4**
		5	**6**
		7	**8**

 © MIMOSA MOVING INTO MATH K **Activity Sheet 25.3**

Dear Family,

During the past week, the children have had many opportunities to work with money. They were all very excited to learn about money as it is such an important part of everyday life.

The children began by identifying pennies and nickels and giving each coin the appropriate name and value; for example, they have been saying things like, *A penny is the same as one cent, and a nickel is the same as five cents.* They were then introduced to the cents sign (¢) and had practice reading price tags up to nine cents. We especially had fun when we pretended to have our own store and we went shopping. The children had several opportunities to act out different situations where they bought and sold objects up to the value of nine cents. This involved counting out the correct number of coins to make their purchases. Going shopping was a very realistic way for the children to use addition and subtraction with money.

You can help your child continue to expand his/her knowledge of addition, subtraction, and money by taking your child shopping with you. Seeing how money is exchanged for different products, how transactions are made, and the role of the cashier are wonderful learning experiences. As you shop, read as many different price tags to your child as you can. If you find any price tags that show a price below ten cents, have your child read them to you.

If your child has saved any pennies, encourage him/her to count the pennies aloud to you. When the value reaches an amount higher than nine cents, you may need to help your child count. Also, encourage your child to tell you about the names of nickels and pennies and how much they are worth.

Thanks for your help with our money unit. As you work with your child, you will see how interesting money is to him/her. I guess money is fascinating to all of us!

Sincerely,

Dear Family,

The children have been busy exploring patterns during the past week. They have been copying, creating, and extending patterns, and they have developed a better awareness of the many patterns that surround us. I have been encouraging them to discuss the patterns they see around them, and the patterns they create.

You can help your child to continue to expand his/her knowledge of patterns by having him/her talk about the patterns that can be found at home. Here are some suggestions:

• If you have any patterned wrapping paper, please give it to your child to play with. Encourage him/her to look for patterns in the paper. Have your child tell you what the pattern is, and why it is a pattern. Have him/her show you where the pattern repeats.

• Another good way of exploring a "realistic" pattern is to show your child a string of beads or a bracelet. Talk about the piece of jewelry with your child, asking questions such as, *What is the pattern in this piece of jewelry? Why is this a pattern? What would come next in the pattern?*

• Show your child a blanket, or a towel, or washcloth that has a pattern, and have him/her talk about the pattern he/she sees, as well as what would come next in the pattern.

• Ask your child to look at his/her own clothes, or in the closet, to see if there are any patterns on the clothes.

Encourage your child to use the accompanying activity sheet to record some of the patterns found at home. He/she can then bring the pictures to school to share.

Thanks for your help. Have fun noticing and talking about patterns.

Sincerely,

Exploring Patterns

Help your child to find some patterns.
Talk with him/her about the patterns and encourage him/her to draw some of them to bring to school to share.

Dear Family,

The children have been listening to stories about equal groups of things, as well as acting out the stories using counters and other hands-on materials. After listening to the stories, the children have had practice answering the following questions: *How many groups? How many in each group? How many in all?* The children have particularly enjoyed listening to these special stories involving equal groups of things.

We have also talked about things that come in groups of two. The children had fun talking about the many things that come in twos, such as shoes, socks, gloves, mittens, boots, slippers, and earrings.

You can help your child gain an even better understanding of equal groups by helping your child complete the accompanying activity. You will need four small containers such as plates or dishes, and ten small cookies or crackers.

Have fun, and thank you for helping your child with this activity. Your help is appreciated. I believe your child can learn even more from a school-related activity when it is followed up at home.

Sincerely,

Equal Groups

Your child will need 4 small containers and 10 small cookies or crackers.
- Please read through the instructions with your child, and put out the number of containers for each story.
- Help him/her to complete the hands-on activity.

Here are 3 plates.
Put 2 cookies on each plate.
How many cookies in all?

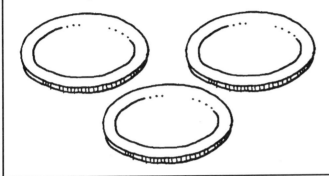

Here are 4 plates.
Put 2 cookies on each plate.
How many cookies in all?

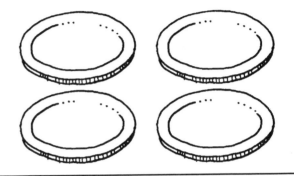

Here are 2 plates.
Put 5 cookies on each plate.
How many cookies in all?

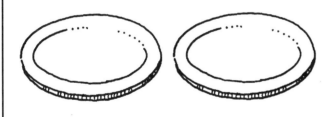

Here are 3 plates.
Put 3 cookies on each plate.
How many cookies in all?

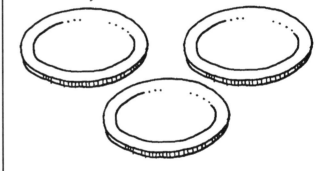

Here are 4 plates.
Put 1 cookie on each plate.
How many cookies in all?

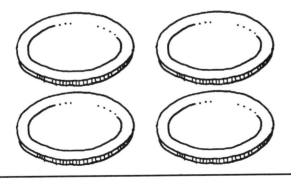

Here are 2 plates.
Put 2 cookies on each plate.
How many cookies in all?

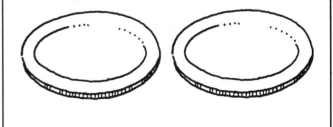

Dear Family,

The children have enjoyed listening to me read and tell stories about sharing things equally. They are learning to be "fair sharers." This means that they are learning to share a given amount of things equally among a group of people. They have also had opportunities to make up and share their own sharing stories with the class. What imaginations!

The children have realised that being fair sharers is important in real-life situations. When they share six crackers among three people, each person wants to eat their two crackers!

You can help your child to continue this learning experience at home by helping him/her to complete the attached sharing activity. Please encourage your child to talk to you about what he/she is doing as he/she explores each situation.

Thank you for your cooperation.

Sincerely,

Fair Shares

Please read through each set of instructions with your child and help him/her to complete this hands-on activity.

Get 4 pencils and share them equally between 2 people.

Show how you will share the pencils.

How many will each person get?

Get 8 cookies and share them equally between 2 people.

Show how you will share the pencils.

How many will each person get?

Get 6 books and share them equally among 3 people.

Show how you will share the books.

How many would each person get?

Find 9 rocks and share them equally between 3 people.

Show how you would share the rocks.

How many would each person get?

Dear Family,

The children have been busy learning about the number "ten." We have been reading stories and rhymes about ten, and the children have had opportunities to tell and write their own stories. We have also been practicing writing the number symbol "10."

The children are intrigued by this fascinating and important number. They have enjoyed making and counting groups of ten objects, and we are even counting, orally, by tens to one hundred. The children feel so smart when they can count by tens from zero to one hundred, especially when they can count quickly.

This is our final math topic for the school year. It has been very rewarding working with your child and I hope that you too have enjoyed sharing your child's math learning. Please try to continue to work with your child during the summer months. Next year, when your child is in Grade 1, you will see many of the skills that were learned this year expanded upon to further your child's mathematical knowledge.

You can help your child increase his/her awareness and understanding of the number ten by helping him/her to complete the accompanying activity at home.

Thank you for your help and cooperation this past school year. I know that your child has appreciated your involvement in his/her learning.

Sincerely,

Exploring Ten

Please read the following directions aloud to your child.

- Find 10 things in the house that are small. Count them aloud for an adult.
- Find 5 things that are smooth and 5 things that are rough. Put them together. How many do you have in all?
- Find 10 things an adult will let you eat. Eat 7 of them. How many are left?
- Find 10 socks. How many pairs of socks is that?
- You will need 5 plates and 10 crackers. Share the crackers so that each plate has the same amount of crackers. How many crackers are on each plate?
- Put 3 blocks under the table and 7 blocks on the table. How many blocks in all do you have?
- If you have 5 bicycles, how many tires is that?
  (Hint: It may help to draw the bicycles and then count the tires.)
- Draw a picture to show ten.

Dear _____ ,

You are invited to come to my school on _____ at _____ to watch me "Move Into Math."

When you visit, I will be able to show you why I enjoy math class. I will show you different ways math relates to the "real" world and reasons why I study math at school. I'm anxious for you to see how I use hands-on materials to solve math problems. Wait until you see how I problem solve — you won't believe it!

When you arrive at my school, please call into the office so that the secretary can direct you to my math classroom, Room ___. I can't wait until you come so that I can share some math experiences with you. It will be an exciting day for me!

My teacher, _____ , wants to know how many people are coming, so could you please cut out and complete the R.S.V.P. form below.

Love, _____

- -

R.S.V.P.

_____ will/will not be coming to the school on _____ to learn more about math.

Signed _____